HOPSCOTCH
STORIES OF
RELIGION

The Loaves
and the Fishes

First published in 2008 by
Franklin Watts
338 Euston Road
London
NW1 3BH

Franklin Watts Australia
Level 17/207 Kent Street
Sydney
NSW 2000

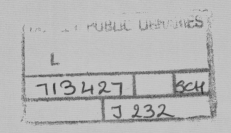

Text © Anita Ganeri 2008
Illustration © Natascia Ugliano 2008

A CIP catalogue record for this book is available
from the British Library.

ISBN 978 0 7496 8370 2 (hbk)
ISBN 978 0 7496 8376 4 (pbk)

Series Editor: Melanie Palmer
Series Advisor: Dr Barrie Wade
Series Designer: Peter Scoulding

Printed in China

Franklin Watts is a division of
Hachette Children's Books,
an Hachette Livre UK company
www.hachettelivre.co.uk

The Loaves
and Fishes
the

by Anita Ganeri and Natascia Ugliano

W
FRANKLIN WATTS
LONDON•SYDNEY

About this book

The story of the Loaves and the Fishes comes from the Bible. The Bible is the name that Christians give to their holy book. They believe that the Bible is the word of God and that it teaches people how God wants them to live and behave. The Bible is divided into two parts, called the Old Testament and the New Testament. The Loaves and the Fishes is found in the Gospels of Matthew (chapter 14; verses 15-21), Mark (chapter 6; verses 35-44), Luke (chapter 9; verses 12-17), and John (chapter 6; verses 5-13). In the story, through the power of God, Jesus performs a miracle and provides food for a huge number of people.

One afternoon, Jesus was out
with his friends, the disciples.

Jesus had spent all day by a lake, teaching the huge crowds about God.

People came from far away
because they wanted to hear
him speak.

"Come," said Jesus to his friends. "We'll take a boat across the lake and find a quiet place to rest."

The disciples cheered. They were looking forward to getting away and having a break.

But when they reached the other
side of the lake, thousands of
people were standing there.

They had heard that Jesus was
coming and had waited all day
to see him.

11

"Please send them away, Jesus," the disciples begged. "It's getting late and everyone is tired."

But Jesus did not listen. He called
to the crowd to come closer and
began talking to them.

As the afternoon turned into
evening, the disciples came up to
Jesus again.

"Send them away, Master," they said. "It's late and everyone is getting hungry."

"Then you must find them something to eat," Jesus told them.

"But there are thousands of people here," Philip, one of the disciples, said. "We can't feed them all!"

Just then, another disciple, Andrew,
came over. He had a small boy
with him, carrying a basket.

"You can have my food,"
the boy said to Jesus and he
handed over the basket.

19

The disciples looked in the basket and saw just two small fishes and five bread rolls. How could that feed thousands of people?

But Jesus turned to the boy.
"Thank you," he said, smiling.

"Put the people into groups,"
Jesus told the disciples. "And tell
everybody to sit down."

Jesus held up the food in his hands
and thanked God for it.

Then he took the five rolls and two fishes and broke them into pieces.

He gave the pieces to the disciples
to share out among the groups.

There was more than enough
food for everyone! The disciples
were amazed.

However fast they shared the food
out, Jesus always had more to give
to them.

Soon everyone was full up on the fish and bread. Then people began to make their way back home.

"Go and collect up the leftovers," Jesus told the disciples. "So that nothing is wasted."

There was so much food left over that the disciples filled twelve big baskets.

Then, at last, the disciples got a well-earned rest and a delicious meal to eat.

Hopscotch has been specially designed to fit the requirements of the Literacy Framework. It offers real books by top authors and illustrators for children developing their reading skills.

ADVENTURES

Aladdin and the Lamp
ISBN 978 0 7496 6692 7

Blackbeard the Pirate
ISBN 978 0 7496 6690 3

George and the Dragon
ISBN 978 0 7496 6691 0

Jack the Giant-Killer
ISBN 978 0 7496 6693 4

TALES OF KING ARTHUR

1. The Sword in the Stone
ISBN 978 0 7496 6694 1

2. Arthur the King
ISBN 978 0 7496 6695 8

3. The Round Table
ISBN 978 0 7496 6697 2

4. Sir Lancelot and the Ice Castle
ISBN 978 0 7496 6698 9

TALES OF ROBIN HOOD

Robin and the Knight
ISBN 978 0 7496 6699 6

Robin and the Monk
ISBN 978 0 7496 6700 9

Robin and the Silver Arrow
ISBN 978 0 7496 6703 0

Robin and the Friar
ISBN 978 0 7496 6702 3

FAIRY TALES

The Emperor's New Clothes
ISBN 978 0 7496 7421 2

Cinderella
ISBN 978 0 7496 7417 5

Snow White
ISBN 978 0 7496 7418 2

Jack and the Beanstalk
ISBN 978 0 7496 7422 9

The Three Billy Goats Gruff
ISBN 978 0 7496 7420 5

The Pied Piper of Hamelin
ISBN 978 0 7496 7419 9

Goldilocks and the Three Bears
ISBN 978 0 7496 7903 3

Hansel and Gretel
ISBN 978 0 7496 7904 0

The Three Little Pigs
ISBN 978 0 7496 7905 7

Rapunzel
ISBN 978 0 7496 7906 4

Little Red Riding Hood
ISBN 978 0 7496 7907 1

Rumpelstiltskin
ISBN 978 0 7496 7908 8

HISTORIES

Toby and the Great Fire of London
ISBN 978 0 7496 7410 6

Pocahontas the Peacemaker
ISBN 978 0 7496 7411 3

Grandma's Seaside Bloomers
ISBN 978 0 7496 7412 0

Hoorah for Mary Seacole
ISBN 978 0 7496 7413 7

Remember the 5th of November
ISBN 978 0 7496 7414 4

Tutankhamun and the Golden Chariot
ISBN 978 0 7496 7415 1

MYTHS

Icarus, the Boy Who Flew
ISBN 978 0 7496 7992 7 *
ISBN 978 0 7496 8000 8

Perseus and the Snake Monster
ISBN 978 0 7496 7993 4 *
ISBN 978 0 7496 8001 5

Odysseus and the Wooden Horse
ISBN 978 0 7496 7994 1 *
ISBN 978 0 7496 8002 2

Persephone and the Pomegranate Seeds
ISBN 978 0 7496 7995 8 *
ISBN 978 0 7496 8003 9

Romulus and Remus
ISBN 978 0 7496 7996 5 *
ISBN 978 0 7496 8004 6

Thor's Hammer
ISBN 978 0 7496 7997 2*
ISBN 978 0 7496 8005 3

No Dinner for Anansi
ISBN 978 0 7496 7998 9 *
ISBN 978 0 7496 8006 0

Gelert the Brave
ISBN 978 0 7496 7999 6*
ISBN 978 0 7496 8007 7

STORIES OF RELIGION

The Good Samaritan
ISBN 978 0 7496 8369 6*
ISBN 978 0 7496 8375 7

The Loaves and the Fishes
ISBN 978 0 7496 8370 2*
ISBN 978 0 7496 8376 4

The Prince and Holika the Witch
ISBN 978 0 7496 8371 9*
ISBN 978 0 7496 8377 1

The Birth of Krishna
ISBN 978 0 7496 8368 9 *
ISBN 978 0 7496 8374 0

The Flight from Makkah
ISBN 978 0 7496 8373 3*
ISBN 978 0 7496 8379 5

The Great Night Journey
ISBN 978 0 7496 8372 6*
ISBN 978 0 7496 8378 8

For more details go to:
www.franklinwatts.co.uk

* **hardback**